This book belongs to

and

Teevra

TO OUR BOYS

Samay   Soham   Naman   Siddharth

© 2016 Little Ustaads Arts Private Limited
This edition published 2018

Published in collaboration with Bloomsbury India

ISBN 978-06-92814-75-8
Printed and bound at EIH Ltd. Gurugram, Haryana

www.littleustaads.com
www.bloomsbury.com

WRITTEN BY

Rachana Chandaria-Mamania and Kavita Bafana

NAMASTE MUMBAI

ILLUSTRATED BY

Sandhya Prabhat

It's 7 o'clock in the morning, the sun rises over the Arabian Sea.
Mumbai, a busy city in India, is buzzing like a bee.

We put on our shoes, grab our cameras and leave the Taj Mahal Hotel,
A place with domes and arches that Mumbaikars know very well.

Hold hands, cross the street, make sure to look both ways.

We reach the square that welcomed King George in his glorious days.

The mighty Gateway of India, stands in the centre of the plaza.
A great place to take a picture with your friends, mummy or papa.

The seagulls circle in the air and the water splashes on the rocks.
All the colourful boats sail to and from the docks.

HURRY! HURRY! The captain is calling
We are going to the Elephanta caves,
The ride is bumpy, Our tummies feel funny,
As we bounce up and down the waves.

There are large trees and big bushes, everywhere I see,
My sister spots a toy train which is perfect for little me.

It's dark and scary inside the tunnel, but I am being brave.
The giant statues are my friends, and I give them all a wave.

Clippity clop, clippity clop,

we can hear the horse carriage coming.

We grab a seat next to the driver,

and giggle at the Bollywood tune he is humming.

The carriage driver welcomes us with a red flower.
Our horses quickly take us to the Rajabai Clock Tower.

The Tower looks like a soldier, standing tall and straight.
The bell inside chimes loudly since 1878.

We reach Chhatrapati Shivaji Terminus, a station that is old and grand.
Everyone is waiting, there is no place to stand.

We run to catch our train, pushing with all our might.
There are so many people packed inside, better hold on tight.

Our tummy starts to grumble,
We are hungry for some snacks.
Look, there's Chowpatty Beach,
And so many yummy food shacks.

We bite into a Mumbai sandwich
Full of tomatoes and cheese.
For dessert we grab an ice gola,
OUCH! we just got a brain freeze!

All Mumbaikars are singing,
It's Ganpati's birthday today.
They celebrate with dancing,
And pray for luck everyday.

The cycling dabbawalas deliver lunch,
While wearing white topis.
People here are so lucky,
They always eat hot rotis!

We climb the stairs to the Hanging Gardens to see the beautiful view.
Boys and girls are playing cricket but that's not what we want to do.

We run across to Kamla Nehru Park, leaving the match behind.
We climb the biggest shoe house that one could ever find!

There are many black and yellow cars honking to get by.
My brother makes me sit in one as the driver finishes his chai.

BEEEP

WELCOME

2316

DELUX

We learn this is a taxi that gets people from place to place.
But to us they look like bumblebees all in a race.

BEEEEP   BEEEEEP   BEEEEP

We whiz across the Worli Sealink to get to Bandra fast.
It feels like we are flying since there is no traffic at last.

We're tired of sitting in the car,
We want to run around.
Luckily, we reach the National Park
To see the monkeys on the ground.

All of a sudden the sky turns grey
And large raindrops hit our head.
Everyone starts to run inside,
But we jump into the puddles instead.

The monsoons have come to Mumbai
You never know when you'll get wet.
Make sure to carry an umbrella
But if your clothes get dirty, don't fret.

It's time for the sun to set, the sky is turning red.
We head to Juhu Beach to see the sun go to bed.

Slowly all the lights come on
And the city begins to shine.
Marine Drive looks like the Queen's necklace
All beautiful and fine.

We drive back to our hotel
and see the lights twinkling like stars.
Everyone is tired, but happy
and returning home in their cars.

It's been a very long day, we want to go to sleep.
All of Mumbai is quiet, there isn't even a peep.

DID YOU SEE?

On how many pages can you spot Teevra the Tiger?

How many seagulls are flying over the Rajiv Gandhi Worli Sealink?

Which two animals can you spot in Hanging Gardens?

What platform is the train leaving from in the Chattrapati Shivaji Terminus?

Who is licking the ice golla at Chowpatty Beach?

How many balloons is the little girl holding at Juhu Beach?

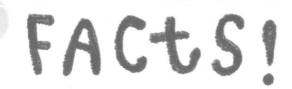

FACTS!

How did Mumbai get its name?

First this city was called **Bom Bahia**, which translates into 'the Good Bay.' Then the British called it **Bombay**. Finally, it was renamed Mumbai after the goddess **Mumba Devi**.

How big is Mumbai?

Mumbai is India's largest city with over **22 million** people. It is the most cramped city in the world.

How did Mumbai become one big city?

Until now, Bombay was a collection of seven separate islands. It took about **150** years to join the seven islands together to make one large Mumbai.

How did planes, trains and automobiles come to Mumbai?

The Juhu Aerodrome was the first airport of India. Chhatrapati Shivaji Terminus (CST) railway station is the first railway station in India. Jamshedji Tata drove the first car in India in 1901 down Marine Drive.

Did you know that Mowgli was created by a Mumbaikar?

Nobel Laureate Rudyard Kipling, who wrote The Jungle Book, was born in Mumbai.

How did Hollywood turn into Bollywood?

The letter 'B' in Bollywood is derived from the city's old name Bombay. Bollywood is one of the largest film producers in the world.

What are those pink birds that visit Mumbai yearly?

15,000 flamingos come to Mumbai yearly between October and March to live in the large marshes and have their babies.

How does everyone in Mumbai get a hot lunch?

The dabbawallas of Mumbai are famous because they never make a mistake. They deliver 200,000 dabbas, or lunchboxes everyday. All dabbawallas wear a white topi, or hat on their heads.

What is the most popular sport in Mumbai?

Cricket is the most popular sport. Maybe you will run into Sachin Tendulkar at Wankhede Stadium practicing his batting.

How can we get to Bandra faster?

The Rajiv Gandhi Worli Sealink connects South Mumbai to Bandra and shortens the time to travel to the suburbs of Mumbai.

What is the most celebrated holiday in Mumbai?

Ganesh Chaturthi is the biggest street festival in Mumbai. Everyone dances around large clay Ganesh statues to celebrate his birth. At the end of the celebration all the idols are immersed in the Arabian Sea.

What are some of the favorite foods Mumbaikars like to eat?

Ice golla - crushed ice with sweet syrup
Roti - round Indian wheat bread
Vada Pav - spicy fried potato fritter served with bread
Pav Bhaji - mixed vegetables with spices served with bread

MUMBAI MAP

NORTH
EAST
WEST
SOUTH

VADA PAV

JUHU BEACH

→ Bandra Worli sealink